G000269745

Penguin Handboo

VOGUE GUIDE TO HA

Felicity Clark has been Beauty Editor of *Vogue* since 1972. She started her career in public relations, and later worked for five years in New York as executive assistant to Diana Vreeland, then editor-in-chief of American *Vogue*. She joined Condé Nast in London in 1969.

As the daughter of a regular army officer, she travelled a lot as a child – and has continued doing so in her job. She was educated at Downe House, is an active sportswoman and a gifted musician – she played the flute in the National Youth Orchestra.

She has worked with leading photographers all over the world. Lord Snowdon says: 'She is one of the most professional editors that I have ever worked with. There are many assignments that I would not have been able to do without her tremendous contribution. It is the back-up that she supplies, the amount of research and meticulous attention to detail that she puts in beforehand. On the assignment itself, she manages to create an atmosphere that stimulates and encourages everyone involved.'

VOGUE GUIDE
TO HAIR CARE

FELICITY CLARK

PENGUIN BOOKS

Penguin Books Ltd, Harmondsworth, Middlesex, England
Penguin Books, 625 Madison Avenue, New York, New York 10022, U.S.A.
Penguin Books Australia Ltd, Ringwood, Victoria, Australia
Penguin Books Canada Ltd, 2801 John Street, Markham, Ontario, Canada L3R 1B4
Penguin Books (N.Z.) Ltd, 182–190 Wairau Road, Auckland 10, New Zealand

First published 1981
Reprinted 1981, 1982

Set in Monophoto Photina by Filmtype Services Limited, Scarborough, Yorks
Made and printed in Great Britain by Butler & Tanner Ltd, Frome & London

Designed by Patrick Yapp

Contents

Introduction

What would Cleopatra have looked like without her geometric cut, where would Botticelli's Venus have been without her flower-strewn curls, how would Lady Godiva have fared without her waist-length hair? Hair has played a vital part in women's fashion – and vanity – since time immemorial. Fairy tales about with descriptions of legendary princesses and their long silken hair. However, some legendary ladies took less notice of their looks and cut off their hair for practical reasons – Joan of Arc and Queen Christina, for instance. Queen Elizabeth I was also practical since, apparently going bald quite early on in her reign, she set the fashion for wigs and possessed a great many. Men too attached enormous importance to their hair – Samson, after all, thought his strength lay in his. Silver and gold wigs were found in the tombs of the Egyptian Pharaohs (less grand men, and women, of that time also wore wigs, made of human hair, wool or palm-leaf fibre).

The Romans cut their hair short, as did Henry VIII centuries later, following the fashion set in France by Francis I (after an accident forced him to cut his off). But long hair and abundant curls returned in the 17th century with King Charles II, developing into the incredible variety of styles of the 18th century and ending with the short cuts of Napoleon and Lord Byron. These lasted in varying forms through the 19th and early 20th centuries until the Beatles re-introduced a fashion for longer hair in the Sixties.

So, for many centuries royalty, rulers, military leaders and the aristocracy set the fashion – but, with modern media like newspapers, cinema and television to entertain and speed news around the world, current trend-setters are more likely to be

LEFT: *Egyptian. Mayet, goddess of truth and justice. Bulky black wig of oiled braids on shaved head.* CENTRE: *Greek. Decadrachma from Syracuse, c.400 B.C. Curled hair loosely tucked into leafed head-band.* RIGHT: *Renaissance. La Primavera by Botticelli. Fashionable flaxen hair, elaborately plaited, curled and bejewelled, one braid forming a necklace.* OPPOSITE LEFT: *Elizabethan. Elizabeth I by Marcus Gheeraets the Younger,*

actors, actresses, pop-stars, sports personalities, politicians or newsreaders. What is obvious is that men and women have always appreciated what their hair can do to improve their looks, and have experimented with shape and colour since the earliest times.

As early as 444 B.C. there is evidence of the use of hair colourants. The early Egyptians wore wigs – mostly black, but some red, blue, green – and they were probably the first people to use henna; the Greeks of the same period used coloured powders (gold, white, red) to tint their natural hair; the Romans bleached with ashes of plants – elderberry, nut-shells, etc. mixed with vinegar sediment – used saffron for yellow and made a black dye from leeches and vinegar fermented in a lead container. There were punks among the Gauls – they dyed their hair bright red with goat's grease and ashes of beech timber – and the Anglo-Saxons coloured their hair green, orange, and blue.

The Roman ladies wished to be blonde and lightened their hair – a fashion that has lasted through the centuries to the present day. Their methods were very damaging to the hair and it was only a matter of time before it was ruined. Methods of lightening improved slightly, however, during the Renaissance when natural infusions of camomile, lupin, myrrh, saffron and gorse were found to have lightening effects on hair; borax and saltpetre were also used for bleaching. Renaissance women also discovered that the sun would lighten their hair and a crownless hat was designed to protect their faces but allow the hair to spread out over the brim and bleach while they sat in the sun. It wasn't until the late 19th

8

c.1592. The elderly queen wears intricately curled red wig, hung with pearl drops. CENTRE: *Late Eighteenth Century. Georgiana, Duchess of Devonshire by Sir Joshua Reynolds. Curled, piled-up and powdered to create maximum volume, this was often achieved by adding pads and tail-pieces.* RIGHT: *Mid Nineteenth Century. Empress Eugénie by Winterhalter. Scanty hair frowned upon, sleek ringlets gathered into a comb.*

century that peroxide was first used, which is, of course, still an essential part of hair colouring today.

Almost every recent hair style can be traced back through history – pony-tails, for instance, to the 15th century – to some fashionable lady or powerful man whose vanity or life-style caused them to experiment with their looks and grow, cut, or curl their hair, add a hairpiece or a wig, and so change the current trend, taking the history of fashion another step forward. They curled their hair with rags or tongs (the ancient Egyptians designed tongs to curl their wigs) – permanent waves were unknown until this century – they cut, braided, rolled, padded, twisted and turned their hair in every conceivable direction. Plaits – for decoration and to hold the hair in place – ribbons, strings of pearls and jewelled circlets were used by the ancient Egyptians, Greeks and Romans and reappear continually through the ages. The Greeks considered a low forehead a mark of great beauty, so their styles arranged the front hair to give this impression; they also made more use of their own hair and less of wigs. The Roman women devised wire frames and padding to raise their hair off their faces. In the Middle Ages there was the simplicity of long flowing hair – sometimes braided or held with a jewelled circlet or looped up under a net – most often worn by young girls before marriage. Married women normally covered their hair. In the 14th and 15th centuries women added width to their faces by coiling braids around their ears, added height by wearing twists of rich jewelled fabrics and diadems, or arranged their hair over pads. In the 16th century women frizzed

9

hair over the forehead, but by mid-century they were turning their hair up and back over pads or wire frames to give height in front, sometimes winging out from a centre parting (Mary, Queen of Scots) or tightly curled to frame the face above a ruff (Queen Elizabeth I). Seventeenth-century women returned to elaborate arrangements of curls and braids, and the 18th century saw the most fantastic hair styles ever known – huge concoctions of curls (usually false) arranged over wire frames and decorated with feathers, flowers, fruit or anything else that could be thought of; these lasted to the turn of the century when there was a revival of early Grecian styles. Mid-century, a simple centre parting returned to fashion, the hair smoothed back over the ears or with ringlets or braids framing the sides of the face and the back taken up into a knot; this fashion lasted through the Victorian era. The Edwardians seemed to have abundant hair; they curled it softly and swept it up, piling the curls high and forward on top of their heads. Hair was bobbed, shingled and Marcel-waved in the Twenties, slightly longer with side-partings and stiff waves in the Thirties; by 1940 women were adapting their hair to the style of the latest film-star; and after the war fashion really began changing rapidly. Now there are so many prevalent styles that every woman can find one to suit her *and* feel she is fashionable. What is different is the depth of knowledge about hair – what it is made of, how it is fed and what makes it grow – bringing scientific hair-care products, and electrical aids to the art of hairdressing, new techniques and expertise to the hairdresser and making it easier for women to ensure the health and looks of their hair.

This book aims to tell you the facts about your hair *now* – how to look after it and find styles that suit you, so that your hair looks its best all the time and you are happy with the way you look. It's not for nothing it's referred to as a woman's crowning glory.

There are two companion books to this one – *Vogue Guide to Skin Care* and *Vogue Guide to Make-up*, also published by Penguin Books.

John Swannell

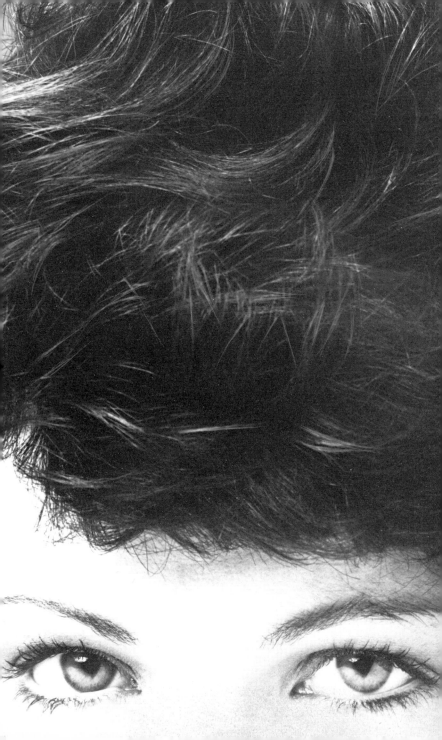

What is Hair?

Most people have around 100,000 strands of hair on their head –
some may have a few thousand less, some many thousands more,
but this is the average, whatever the texture. Red-heads, although
they have the thickest hair, have the least strands; brunettes come
next; and blondes, with the finest hair, have the most strands.
Paradoxically, blond hair can often look limp and thin while red
hair looks abundantly thick. Each strand starts below the surface of
the skin in a little nodule known as the *papilla*, which, even when a
hair is plucked out 'by the roots', is left behind to start again and
eventually produce a new hair. The *root* is the section of the hair
below the skin's or scalp's surface – the visible part above,
whatever its length, is the *shaft*. The root is enclosed in a sac called
the *hair follicle*, the base of which forms the papilla. Each strand,
even though the outward appearance may vary from person to
person, has the same basic structure of three layers. The innermost
layer or *medulla* is soft and spongy, providing a small amount of
colour from cells sometimes containing granules of colour pigment; this is surrounded by the *cortex*, composed of long thin cells,
which provides elasticity and most of the colour; lastly there is the
outer layer, or *cuticle*, which consists of overlapping scales designed
to protect the other two layers. The papilla receives a blood supply
enabling it to produce the hair. The quality of this blood determines
the strength of the hair. It makes sense, therefore, to make sure that
your daily diet includes not only the vitamins and minerals
essential for a healthy body, but those particularly beneficial to
hair, i.e., lots of protein (hair is 97% protein, 3% moisture) and

vitamin B (Brewers' Yeast tablets are a good source of this) – and to cut down on sugar, salt and animal fats. The diet that is good for healthy hair is good for the rest of you.

The minute the hair leaves the follicle, i.e., when it shows on the surface and becomes the shaft, it is, to all intents and purposes, dead. It is no longer receiving nourishment from the papilla and its health and condition will depend on outside help. This period of 'rest' in the life-span of the hair strand will continue for as much as six years, until it eventually falls out and is replaced by a new hair manufactured in the same papilla. The growth cycle is 'staggered' from hair to hair and distributed over the scalp, so that when hairs fall out through this natural process it is unnoticeable in the general amount of hair on the head; up to a hundred hairs a day should be accepted as quite normal. Only when daily 'fall-out' is abnormally large should it be seen as a warning signal and steps be taken to locate the cause and treat it.

There are oil-glands attached to the hair follicles secreting natural oils, but not enough to reach far along the shaft; once the hair grows to any length, the ends certainly never get fed. This

RIGHT: *A highly magnified photograph illustrating the thread-like fibres within the inner structure or the cortex of the hair.*

OPPOSITE LEFT: *A highly magnified shot of a hair that has been damaged by improper care. It illustrates how the layers of the cuticle have separated and shows how easily this hair would become entangled during styling and thus be harder to work on than healthy undamaged hair.*

OPPOSITE RIGHT: *A microscopic enlargement of a split hair. There is no known chemical remedy to heal a 'split end' and it can only be cured by cutting it off.*

Wella International

14

means, of course, that the ends become starved as they get older and are most vulnerable to damage. Cutting off dry brittle ends will stop them from splitting and leave the hair looking fuller and healthier – and sometimes give the impression of faster-growing hair. This, however, is an illusion – it is not possible to alter the hair's growth-pattern, which is fixed when you are conceived. The average growth is around half an inch ($1 \cdot 3$ cm) a month, which slows as you grow older, and, although individuals may have a faster or slower growth-rate, it is not affected by cutting the hair. Some people have difficulty growing their hair to any length at all while others seem to get it to reach their waist in no time. This is because of the combination of growth-rate and life-span: hair that seems hardly to grow at all combines a slow growth-rate with a short life-span; those lucky enough to possess a fast growth-rate with a long life-span can grow long hair quickly. This combination, like the texture of your hair, is hereditary and there is nothing you can do to alter it. The colour and curliness of your hair, although also determined by ancestry, can be changed with modern chemicals.

Hair Types

If your hair doesn't please you, it will affect the way you look and feel. So the more you know about your type of hair, the more you'll be able to do with it and the less you'll try to expect impossible things from it. The first and most important thing you need to know is what type of hair you have. Is it oily, dry or mixed? Has it been permed or straightened? Has the colour been altered by tinting or bleaching? You need to answer all these questions before working out a hair-care routine. Next, you need to study its thickness and texture and curling ability to determine the variety of styles in which it will behave well and, bearing in mind the shape of your face, height, weight and life-style, eliminate those that are unsuitable. The combination of correct hair-care routine plus suitable hair style will make sure you are getting the maximum from this vital part of your beauty image.

Oily Hair
Oily hair almost always goes with oily skin and frequently with fine hair. A certain amount of oil is vital for hair and skin, but when the oil-glands produce more than can be absorbed problems begin. Oily hair is easily recognizable as it becomes lank soon after shampooing and then quickly looks greasy and in need of another wash.

It used to be thought that frequent shampooing stimulated the glands into producing even more oil, but current thinking is that a clean scalp is essential to the control of greasy hair and, providing

the correct shampoo is used, it doesn't matter even if it is washed as much as twice a day. The rule is: wash whenever your hair looks or feels in need.

For oily hair, use the mildest, blandest shampoo you can find. Use the shampoo sparingly, wash your hair and scalp gently – don't scrub or over-massage – and rinse scrupulously, finishing with cold water. Sometimes greasy hair needs conditioning, but only if the ends are dry or split – in this case, apply conditioner only on the dry ends and use as little as possible, rinsing off well. After shampooing or between shampoos it helps to cleanse the scalp with an astringent lotion. The method is to part the hair in sections, soak a cotton-wool ball in the lotion and wipe it down the partings – until you have covered the whole scalp; witch-hazel and the juice of a lemon diluted in water are excellent. Diet is important in the control of greasy hair – cut out animal fats, fried foods, carbohydrates, eggs, nuts, alcohol, salad dressing. Step up intake of low-fat protein (like white fish or chicken), raw vegetables, salads and fresh fruit and drink lots and lots of water.

Dry Hair
Dry hair occurs when too little oil is secreted from the glands attached to the hair follicle or the hair shaft is damaged by bleaching or frequent exposure to the elements – wind, sun, salt or chlorine-filled water or central heating, all of which cause the natural moisture to evaporate. If dry hair is a permanent problem, the sufferer will probably have dry skin too, but if it is caused by external damage to the hair shaft, particularly by bleaching, it could be combined with any skin type (although over-exposure to harsh elements causes devastating damage to skin too). Dry hair is hard to control, full of electricity and lacks lustre, with little ends sticking up all over the place. Permanent or hereditary dry hair is not helped by infrequent shampooing. You might think that shampooing washes away the natural oils and dries out the hair even further, but in fact lack of washing only results in a dirty

scalp. Dry hair, like all hair conditions, needs a clean scalp to allow the hair follicles and sebaceous glands to function with maximum efficiency – and shampooing and conditioning with the correct products is essential. Self-inflicted dry hair – caused by over-bleaching, over-tinting or over-exposure to outside elements – is easier to treat because the problem is with the hair shaft, which is continually being renewed, and not with the papilla, where the hair is formed. Dandruff, in severe cases, can cause dry hair. This is often because, in an attempt to cure the dandruff, the wrong shampoo is being used, which prevents the natural oils from reaching the base of the hair shaft. You should find a shampoo specially formulated for dry hair and always use a conditioner. An oil treatment once or twice a week before shampooing can do wonders too: warm some olive oil or a light vegetable oil and part the hair down the middle; apply from forehead to nape, then work down the sides in sections until the whole head is saturated. Use your fingers to massage the oil into the scalp and hair, then wrap your hair in plastic (cling-film is excellent) and cover with a towel, preferably warm, which will cause moisture to build up under the plastic. The longer you can leave this treatment on, the better; overnight is ideal. In the morning the oil can be removed by two washes with shampoo. A correct diet is essential in treating permanent and self-inflicted dry hair – you need to ensure that the blood feeding the papilla is rich enough and that there is enough oil in your system, so step up your intake of low-cholesterol polyunsaturated oils (eat margarine, make salad dressings from sunflower oil or light vegetable oils, eat low-fat cheese and yogurt), raw vegetables and fruit, take a supplement of vitamin E oil capsules and cut down on carbohydrates, alcohol and spicy foods.

Mixed Condition Hair
Mixed condition hair is the combination of an oily scalp with dry hair. The scalp may *feel* dry and be flaking with dandruff scales, but the hair shaft is drying out because the oil secreted from the glands

in the follicle is soaking into the dandruff flakes, clogging the follicle and preventing the flow of oil along the hair shaft.

The first step to cure this condition is to clear the scalp of flaking scales by using a mild anti-dandruff shampoo or a lotion applied after the head has been shampooed and conditioned. After the scaling has cleared, use a shampoo for dry hair, a conditioner and then an astringent or anti-dandruff lotion to ensure that the scalp remains clear. Avoid animal fats, fried foods, carbohydrates, eggs, nuts, alcohol, salad dressings – and concentrate on low-fat protein (white fish, chicken), raw vegetables, salads, fresh fruit (no bananas) and lots of water.

Balanced or Normal Hair

This is the ideal hair condition, one that everyone strives and longs for. Balanced hair is shiny, well-behaved and doesn't cry out for washing too frequently. The scalp is clear, the sebaceous glands producing the right amount of oil to flow along the shaft, and probably the rest of the body is in excellent order too – a balanced, nutritious diet is followed, regular exercise is taken and the facial skin is in good condition. However, even this hair will not remain wonderful for long if it is not given due care and attention. A careless holiday in the sun, a course of antibiotics (or other medication), a binge of overeating, a broken limb causing inactivity, a bad perm or tint – any of these can upset the delicate balance of the scalp and hair and cause problems.

Use a mild shampoo as often as necessary; always condition and rinse thoroughly; after the hair has been exposed to any stress (sun or wind, for instance), give it a deep conditioning treatment.

What Happens to Hair at What Age?

From Birth to Ten

The amount of hair on your head is decided before you are born, and the size of the circumference of each follicle is fixed irrevocably. The pregnant woman cannot alter the amount of hair her child will be born with or its type or texture, but she can, by taking proper care of herself and eating nutritious food, ensure that her child's hair has the best possible start.

Fewer follicles than the average doesn't necessarily mean that the hair will be thinner, because the diameter of each follicle may be wider in compensation, causing the hair shaft to be thicker. People with thin hair usually have the most hair follicles, those with thick hair the least. Babies are often born with a considerable amount of hair which falls out in the first few weeks and then begins to grow again.

The age at which a baby starts growing hair varies from child to child, but by the time it is three or four you will know what type of hair it will have. Every time a small baby is bathed its scalp should also be washed and this routine can be a very healthy one to carry on throughout life; mothers should be taught to avoid putting any pressure on the soft spot at the crown (the fontanelle) that babies are born with but not to be so frightened that they don't wash it at all! Lack of routine washing of the scalp can cause a condition known as *cradle cap* – this is a brownish, scaly patch which can spread all over the baby's scalp if not checked by treatment. It can also be caused by a fault in feeding. Cradle cap is treated with warm oil (olive, nut or light vegetable); soak cotton wool in the oil and dab it lightly over the scalp, then wash off with baby soap.

When the child's hair is grown and its type determined, choose a suitable shampoo and conditioner, wash frequently and keep an eye on the scalp and hair for any changes in condition due to climate, environment or age.

Problems: children's heads, even in this day and age, can become infested with fleas and lice – more prevalent in long hair than short; if this happens, go to a doctor for treatment. Ringworm is another infection that children are susceptible to up to the age of puberty. It looks like a circular scaly patch, about half an inch in diameter, sometimes with a pinkish centre; again the child should be taken to the doctor for treatment.

The better balanced a child's diet, the better chance it has of healthy hair – junk food, sugar and too many dairy products are all as detrimental to hair as they are to general body health. If a child can be persuaded to *like* fruit, fruit juices, raw or dried fruits and yogurt instead of sugar-based drinks, sweets, crisps and ice-creams, it will feel enormous benefit for the rest of its life.

The Teens

The hormonal changes that occur with puberty can have a dramatic effect on hair. The male and female hormones pouring through a child's bloodstream cause hair to appear on parts of the body other than the head. Boys need to start shaving, girls start thinking about unwanted hair on legs, underarms and lips. Both sexes develop pubic hair.

It is a time of tremendous activity in the body and at the same time the adolescent is often under pressure and studying for important exams. Stress can be reflected in the health of hair at any time, but it is most likely in the teens.

Hormonal changes often cause oily hair, the glands being stimulated into over-production of oil, which floods the hair shaft, gives an overall effect of lank greasiness and often produces a bad odour. The hair should be washed every day – twice a day, if necessary – with a shampoo formulated for oily hair; if a conditioner is used, only apply it to the ends. To prevent odour, all oily and fatty foods, sugar, salt, spice and dairy products must be avoided; if he or she is a junk-food addict, this habit must be broken. Dandruff is another problem often first encountered at this time and care must be taken that the dandruff treatment does not aggravate the oily condition of the hair. The cause of this dandruff is often tension and (as with oily hair) the treatment is to alter diet and encourage scrupulous cleansing of the scalp. Extra vitamin B will often help. In mild cases a shampoo for oily hair will usually control the dandruff, but severe cases may need special treatment such as a medicated shampoo containing sulphur or zinc pyrithione.

Problems: split ends are very prevalent amongst teenagers–often caused by over-enthusiastic use of electrical equipment. In finding hair styles that suit and in keeping pace with changing moods, teenagers overuse blow driers, heated rollers, styling brushes and curling tongs. They are impatient and feel they haven't the time to let their hair dry gently with the dryer on 'low' – everything is done at top speed and on the highest setting, which is fine for saving time but disaster for the hair: a too-hot dryer can burn the scalp and dry out the hair shaft; heated rollers taken out in a hurry can tangle the hair really badly and, if used too often, dry out the ends. The answer for split ends is to cut them off – if you catch them soon enough it makes little difference to the overall length of hair – and never allow them to spread right up the hair shaft. It is better still to prevent them appearing by using electrical aids carefully and making sure the hair is well conditioned and not allowed to dry out. *Trichotillomania* is the term for the mania for pulling out one's own hair to the extent of causing bald patches – girls of eleven to fourteen and menopausal women are susceptible. It is thought to have two main causes: an unconscious need for masochistic sexual gratification, a side-effect of sexual fantasies; or an unconscious need for extra attention from someone close. The cure is to find the cause – in the first case, the child will probably soon grow out of the habit; in the second, extra understanding of the teenager's confused state of mind, tolerance of unpredictable moods and patient kindness will probably do the trick, but in either case a visit to a qualified trichologist will help.

The Twenties

The twenties should be a time of maximum health in every respect. Hormones have settled down, adolescent problems are over, the body should be in peak condition, worries about ageing a long way off and all the excitement of the future ahead. But, on the negative side, this is when many women start to abuse their hair by over-colouring, perming, straightening – *anything* to be fashionable! – and when sun and wind damage begin to be noticeable after a few years of regular holidays in the sun, on the sea or skiing. Many women become pregnant in their twenties and may suffer from hair loss either during pregnancy or shortly after the birth – or this may happen with a second or third child for the first time. The prime concern of the body is to nourish the unborn child and, if the woman's diet is low in essential nutrients, like iron, calcium, and protein, there may be insufficient blood, oxygen and food nutrient supplies to satisfy the unborn child, its mother and her hair. Pregnancy hair loss cannot be prevented, but proper care and diet will reduce the quantity and ensure healthy regrowth.

Sun damage – either from summer or winter sun – demands instant re-conditioning. A good treatment is warm olive oil (or a light vegetable oil) applied to the hair, massaged in and covered in plastic film. Wrap the head in a warm towel and leave for as long as possible – overnight is ideal – before shampooing out. Then try to prevent the damage recurring by taking preventative steps: cover your hair with a scarf in wet or windy weather; rinse out salt- or chlorine-filled water immediately, then shampoo and condition; use protective lotions on your hair before going out in the sun.

Oily hair occurring at this age is normally due to a bad washing routine, incorrect shampoo or a persistently poor diet. Don't wash in hot water, but use warm: rinse in cooler water, finishing with a cold rinse; try a less rich shampoo and make sure it is designed for oily hair; check diet for a high intake of fatty, sugary or spicy foods and cut them out.

Coarse hair can be a problem in the twenties, when the extra oils produced in adolescence have subsided, leaving the coarse hair in a drier, bushier condition. Wash with a shampoo for dry hair, condition with a cream rinse, combing it with a wide-toothed comb, and comb the hair into place while it's still wet and pliable.

The Thirties

Hair may start to dry out as the oil-producing glands begin to slow down; regular, richer hair-conditioning treatments will improve its health. Dryness may also be the result of years of bleaching, colouring and permanent waving; after many of these processes it is essential to re-condition the hair, as the harsh chemicals will have stripped it of most of its natural oil and moisture, leaving the hair shafts lack-lustre and brittle.

Hair loss is often a by-product of stress in the thirties. Career or marriage problems, responsibilities of parenthood, all begin to pile up; one of the first signs of this sort of tension is hair loss. If the stress is reduced, hair will regrow, because the papilla is only waiting for the right conditions to start manufacturing again. But if the stress continues and becomes worse the hair loss will become more serious and treatment for both conditions is essential. Poor health can also cause hair loss, for while the body is using all its resources to recover from illness it cannot nourish the hair.

Grey hairs can appear at any age, but by thirty most people have a few and are wondering why. Each strand of hair contains *melanin*, or colour granules, and those which have no melanin at all are white. Some people are born with white strands, some teenagers acquire them at puberty, but mostly they begin to appear as the hair ages. As with all other forms of ageing, certain processes slow down, and in this case it is the formation of colour pigment in

25

the cortex of the hair shaft. As the colour pigment fails to form, it is replaced with air space, making the hair strand appear white or grey. The grey effect comes from the mixture of white and coloured hairs. Heredity plays a part in deciding when you will start going grey; it is thought that stress and worry and lack of vitamins such as vitamin B, which is essential to healthy hair, do too.

Another, fairly unusual, problem of the thirties is a particularly severe type of dandruff, which is actually a form of psoriasis. The flakes appear larger than normal dandruff, worse after shampooing and the scalp may suffer from irritable red patches. A shampoo containing coal extract should control the condition, but if it persists, consult an expert.

The Forties

During the forties the problems of ageing, which may have started to show in the thirties, become more prevalent – dry hair, dandruff, grey hair and hair that has lost its colour and life.

The dryness is caused by a further slowing down in the production of oil by the sebaceous glands and will usually be a problem in skin all over the body too. Use a rich shampoo for dry hair, leave hair conditioner on a little longer and give hair a deep conditioning treatment at least once a week. Dry hair naturally if possible or with a low heat to avoid loss of natural moisture.

Dandruff is usually the dry-scalp variety and dandruff shampoos are not necessarily the answer. Try a shampoo for dry hair, massaging the scalp as you lather; rinse thoroughly to cleanse the scalp of all loose flakes and, if this doesn't solve the problem, try alternating with a dandruff shampoo.

Grey hair can be disguised with products specially formulated to cover grey hair. Choose a colour near your natural colour for the best effect; better still, go to a professional colourist.

Dull hair means that the light is reflected evenly or not reflected at all and the hair looks drab and lifeless. A colour conditioning rinse, tint or sometimes henna will restore the lustre and gloss.

Mrs Sheila Ogden photographed by David Montgomery

Fifty and Over

At this age most women have reached the menopause and, along with the other problems associated with this time, hair and scalp suffer from the change in hormonal balance that is occurring and the stress that is often present. The hair follicles are not receiving the support from hormones that they are used to and this may result in hair loss. Facial hair may coarsen or darken. Women receiving hormone treatment during menopause will probably find the hair fall less severe, but there is no reason why any woman should suffer distressing hair loss during menopause, providing she looks after her hair and scalp, cares for her body with proper diet and exercise and generally maintains her health.

Excessive hair fall, at any age, is something to take seriously, and professional advice should be sought. Dandruff at this time could be due to lack of circulation – massage, while the hair is being shampooed, will help, loosening scalp cells and stimulating blood flow. A soft hair style that doesn't need spraying into place, allows the hair to be brushed through and the scalp massaged between shampoos will also help this type of dandruff.

Greying hair will also become drier, needing a good rich shampoo and conditioner, and the scalp must be kept clean.

27

Hair Care

Healthy hair is always high on any list of important beauty assets. Correct hair-care routine is vital if it's to look its best all the time. How can you arrive at the correct routine for your hair? First, establish your hair type – is it oily, dry, mixed or normal? Then its texture – is it fine, medium or coarse? Is it thick or thin? Curly or straight? Choose products especially formulated for your hair type.

Shampooing

You can shampoo your hair every day if you like – twice a day if necessary. The modern rule is: wash whenever it looks or feels in need; the vital thing is to use a mild shampoo that is correctly formulated for your type of hair.

The key to healthy hair is a healthy scalp, which allows the hair follicles and the sebaceous glands attached to them to function efficiently. Don't scrub as you wash; treat your hair as gently as fabric and massage the scalp as you lather. Carelessness at this stage can harm your hair. A good method is to soak your hair first in warm water, then apply the shampoo. Don't use too much shampoo – many are very concentrated; it does no harm to dilute in a little water before applying – and make sure the shampoo is spread evenly through your hair. A good trick to ensure this is to pour it first into the palms of your hands, rub them together and then apply to your hair. You can always add more shampoo if you need it. Then rinse, rinse and rinse again – there is no point in spending hours styling your hair if it isn't clean when you start.

If you wash your hair very frequently you probably need only one application each time – too much shampoo too often will strip the hair shaft of all the natural oils it needs to provide the lustre and manageability you are looking for.

To find the right shampoo for your hair may take a little experimenting. First read the labels to find one that is designed for your kind of hair – they should tell you (apart from whether they are for oily, dry or balanced hair) whether they have a medicated ingredient for dandruff, are hypo-allergenic, have an additive to treat tinted or bleached hair, are enriched to control flyaway hair and whether they are based on natural or plant extracts. Many will refer to a pH factor – this is the measure of the liquid's acidity or alkalinity. Hair is surrounded by a liquid mantle of atmospheric moisture, perspiration and so forth. Ideally this liquid mantle should be slightly acidic. Many of the things we routinely do to hair, like colouring, permanent waving and straightening, even shampooing, can leave an alkaline residue. This alkalinity can weaken the hair's structure, making it less resilient or elastic and thus more prone to breaking and splitting. The pH products are aimed at maintaining the natural acid/alkaline balance of the hair's moisture mantle, but should only be necessary for chemically altered hair – i.e., that which has been coloured, bleached, permed or straightened.

Dry shampoos mostly come in powder form and are based on talc or cornstarch. The method is to shake a little into the hair, distribute it by rubbing gently so that it absorbs oil and dirt and then brush it out. Its best use is for people with oily hair and for fringes, which tend to become oily more quickly than the rest of the head. Alternatively, dabbing the scalp with an astringent lotion, witch-hazel or eau-de-Cologne will usually do the trick.

Conditioning
A conditioner for your hair is like a moisturizer for your skin – after cleansing you use a moisturizer, after shampooing you should use

a conditioner. The purpose of a conditioner is to counteract dryness of the hair shaft, to smooth and make it manageable by making it easier to comb through and style and to help prevent split ends and breakage.

When you consider that any single strand of hair on your head can be as old as six years – which means six years of exposure to sun, wind, water, curling, brushing, styling and probably tinting, perming or straightening, it is no wonder it is no longer in its original healthy condition and needs all the help it can get.

The moment the hair appears on the scalp and leaves its follicle beneath the skin it ceases to receive nourishment from the papilla – the only help it gets is from the oil-glands attached to the follicle, which should provide enough oil to flow down the shaft and condition it. However, all abuses tend to strip the hair shaft of this natural lubrication and the ends especially become very dry and brittle.

Clive Arrowsmith

A conditioner is, therefore, a vital part of your hair-care routine if it's to stay healthy and glossy. There are instant conditioners and cream rinses to use each time you shampoo, and deep-penetrating conditioning treatments to use once or twice a week, if the hair is damaged or very dry; or once a month, for healthy maintenance.

After shampooing, hair has a negative electric charge, the degree of which depends on the humidity and the shampoo; it can be greater on some days than on others. It makes each hair strand stand away from its neighbour, causing flyaway hair, and conditioners compensate by adding a positive electric charge.

The method of applying conditioner is similar to shampooing except that you don't need to pre-rinse as the hair is already wet and pliable from rinsing off the shampoo. Use conditioners sparingly and start by putting a small amount in the palms of your

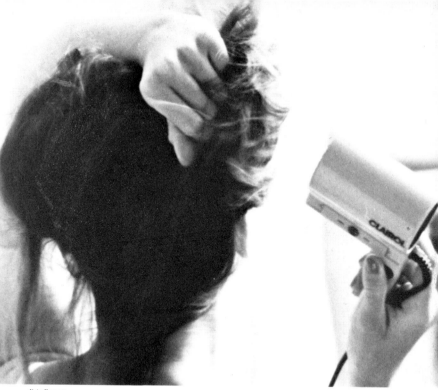

Eric Boman

hands, rubbing them together and applying flat to your hair. Then, with your fingers, comb the conditioner through your hair and along the hair shafts and leave it on for a minute. Rinse off very thoroughly. Finish with a cold-water rinse, which helps make hair shinier because it closes the scales on the outer layer or cuticle of the hair shaft, making them all lie in one direction and thus providing a smoother surface.

Deep conditioning treatments are essential to restore damaged or dried-out hair at the end of a summer or winter sports holiday, or if the hair has been over-bleached or tinted or badly permed. Some – particularly home-made conditioners containing olive, nut or light vegetable oils – are applied before shampooing, preferably the night before; others are applied afterwards and left on between ten and thirty minutes before being rinsed out.

Recipes for Shampoos and Conditioners

Shampoo

Try the oldest shampoo of all – the herb saponaria or soapwort. You can buy the dried root in packets (it is often used to clean old and delicate fabrics).

Put 0·9 oz. (25 g) of saponaria with 1¾ pints (1 litre) of water into a non-aluminium pan, bring to the boil, then simmer for 20 minutes, stirring occasionally. Let it stand until cool, then strain through muslin. Make up the liquid to 1¾ pints (1 litre) with a strong infusion of another herb such as camomile (for fair hair), rosemary (for dark hair) or nettle (for scalp problems).

Conditioner

Mashed avocado or beaten eggs work wonders on dull lifeless hair – leave on for 15–20 minutes, then rinse well – but probably the best home hair treatment of all is warm oil.

Heat a small amount of olive oil, or any good vegetable oil, to blood temperature. About ¼ pint (0·14 litres) should be enough. Apply it to the scalp by parting the hair in sections, until the whole head is thoroughly saturated, then comb through with a wide-toothed comb and massage the scalp. Finally wrap the head in tinfoil or a plastic cap and cover with a warm towel. Leave on overnight if possible, then wash twice with a good mild shampoo and rinse thoroughly.

Rinse

To help hair shine and keep the scalp healthy, make a final rinse from the juice of a fresh lemon diluted in really cold water – this closes the pores on the scalp and makes the overlapping scales on the hair shaft lie flat and reflect the light.

Quick pick-ups

Powdered orris root is a natural dry shampoo; the hair should be divided in sections and the powder scattered down the partings. Leave for five minutes, then brush out thoroughly. A good tip is to cover the brush with a piece of absorbent fabric (muslin, gauze or nylon) sprinkled with a mild astringent like witch-hazel or eau-de-

Eric Boman

Cologne – this will help remove grease and dust and speed up the process of removing the powder.

Alternatively the astringent alone can be massaged into the scalp down the partings – this will act as a temporary dry-clean and is useful if someone is bedridden and cannot move their head.

Brushing and Combing

In the days when there were no such things as conditioners and ladies had waist-length hair, there might have been some sense in the old rule: 'brush a hundred strokes a day'. But today excessive brushing can put such stress on hair that it splits, breaks or comes out at the roots, especially if it has been chemically altered or is very dry. Brushing also spreads scalp conditions, dirt and debris, so if you like to do it, the brush itself must be kept absolutely clean. Only brush hair when it is absolutely dry – wet hair is particularly vulnerable to breakage from brushing.

As a general rule, combing is best, but if brushing is vital to the style, keep it to a minimum and finish putting the hair in place with a comb. Always let the hair cool before removing rollers and remove the bottom ones first to avoid tangling the hair; then brush or comb straight back, but gently, to distribute the waves evenly. Don't drag it or you will run the risk of pulling it out by the roots or breaking the strands.

Bending over and brushing from the nape to the forehead is good for the scalp, as it stimulates circulation, and also adds fullness to the hair.

Drying
After shampooing and conditioning, the next step in hair care is drying. As much damage can be caused at this stage as any other and it is important to dry your hair the right way. The best way is to let it dry naturally, but many people haven't the time for this, so this is the next best method.

First blot out excess water with a towel. Then comb hair through using a wide-toothed comb, starting at the ends and working towards the scalp, removing tangles as you go. With another dry towel blot out any further moisture by wrapping it smoothly around your head and squeezing it around the ends. Then set and blow-dry or sit under the drier. Don't over-dry – if you can find the time, let the heated air cool off; then dry naturally for the last few minutes. This will prevent any danger of the hair shaft drying out and being damaged.

Blow-drying must be done with care to avoid the hair tangling and breaking off. Divide it into sections and, as you dry, lift each section of hair up and away from the scalp and wrap round a brush. Plastic ones with widely spaced, soft, elastic bristles are best. Now blow the section dry, working from the root to the end of the strands. Start at the back, at the nape of the neck (pin the rest of the hair on top of your head to get it out of the way), work around the sides, around the face and lastly dry the crown.

Mike Reinhardt

Hair Styles

One of the most important things to know about your hair is its limitations. Learn to live with them. This means accepting your hair's texture. If it is fine, it probably tends to be flyaway and doesn't hold a set well. If it's medium, it probably behaves itself quite well and holds a set. If it's coarse, it is probably unruly and hard to curl. It also means accepting the amount of hair you have – its body or bulk. If the hairs on your head are massed and close together, your hair is thick. If they're sparse, your hair is thin. The amount of straightness or curliness imposes some limitations, though perming or straightening can usually correct this. You are born with these qualities and there is nothing you can do to change them, so make the best of them. Fine hair is usually thin and looks fullest and best when it's blunt-cut and not much longer than chin length. Medium-textured hair with medium body can take almost any kind of style or length – it has the fewest limitations. Coarse hair often responds well to a longish blunt-cut. The length tends to weight the hair down and make it behave. Too short a cut is apt to leave you with hair that bushes and sticks out.

If hair is curly, humidity will make it curl more. Chemical straightening can be a solution, if you insist on a straight look.

Straight hair, especially if it's fine, will usually resist curling except under good weather conditions. So again, your best plan is to find a style that doesn't rely too much on curl, unless you invest in a good permanent wave. This, depending on how fast your hair grows, is a fairly temporary solution and can be expensive if your hair needs re-perming often. However, modern soft perms are very good indeed and do offer the straight-haired person the chance of a complete change of look.

How to Make a Top Knot

1. *Hair must be long enough to scoop up off the face, without leaving too many loose strands. Beforehand, brush hair forward to give it body and then smoothly back off the face.* **2.** *Take all the hair from above the ears and around the face up to the crown and hold it while the back section is combed in to join it.* **3.** *Hold the hair tightly in place where the finished knot will be, twist it until it coils around neatly and the ends can be tucked in.* **4.** *Finally secure the knot with grips or ornamental hairpins.* **5.** OPPOSITE *The finished effect: a neat small head, cool and comfortable for summer.*

Sandra Lousada

Blow-Drying and Rollers

1. *With this good basic cut, several things can be done: it can be blow-dried for a sleek, barely curved look; set with heated rollers for the curly look, or with a combination of regular rollers and a hand drier for a long-lasting pageboy.* **2.** *For the curly look: Blow-dry the hair, not to style it but just to dry and smooth it. Then set with medium-sized rollers, two on top, three on each side, two turned under, one close to the face rolled forward. The back is set in one row of large rollers rolled to the nape. When the rollers have cooled, unroll them, brush hair gently into shape. For extra hold try one of the wetting-plus-conditioner products made especially for use with heated rollers.* **3.** *For the pageboy: For more hold than just a blow-dry will give, use a large regular roller clipped to the scalp on either side and two in the back. Let blow-drier heat set them for a minute or two.* **4.** *For added fullness on top use four rollers, and two pin curls for the shorter side.* **5.** OPPOSITE *The soft, curly look.*

Mike Reinhardt

Cutting your Hair from Long to Short

1. *The change cutting makes can be dramatic, as it is here: from shoulder length to three-inch layer at the back with shorter hair in front. This looks even shorter as the model's hair is also naturally curly.* **2.** *After shampooing, the hair is cut in sections from front to back so that it can be seen how the new shape suits the model's face, and if necessary be adjusted. The length at the sides is carefully watched so that the hair does*

not get pushed up by ears. **3.** Halfway through the cutting it is already apparent how flattering this style is to the model's face. **4.** The hair is kept wet while cutting. **5.** The hair continues to be cut in sections, as the nape is neared. **6.** An anti-static and light setting lotion is rubbed through, and the hair is towelled dry. **7.** It is finally finger dried, and when completely dry the roots are sprayed again to bring out the curl and left to dry naturally into the finished shape. **8.** The dramatic result.

Sandra Lousada

Glossary of Recent Cuts and Styles

◁ AFRO *Penn*

BLUNT *Sandra Lousada*

BOB   △ BUN *Clive Arrowsmith*   ▽ CAP

△ CHIGNON *Masami Kume*   ▽ CORNROWING *Willie Christie*

△ COUPE SAUVAGE

▽ CURLY *Sandra Lousada*

FRENCH PLEAT *Sandra Lousada*
GEORGE *Mike Reinhardt*

GEOMETRIC *Sandra Lousada*
LAYERED

LONG *John Sw*

MEDIUM *Sandra Lousada*
PAGEBOY

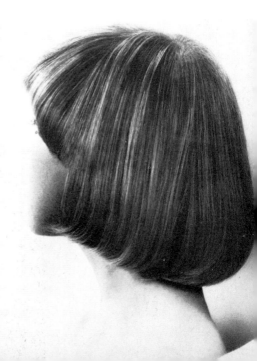

PLAITS *Fouli Elia*
PUNK *Masami Kume*

PONYTAIL *Sandra Lousada*
SHORT *Sandra Lousada*

STRAIGHT
URCHIN

WASH & WEAR *Uli Rose* ▽   **WAVY** *Sandra Lousad*

Special Occasions: Style and Decoration

Many people make the mistake of changing their hair style for a special occasion so drastically that their family and friends hardly recognize them – that's fine if the new style is an improvement, but often it's done with no forethought as to whether it suits them or not. It is vital to try out the transformation you have in mind before the actual moment of wearing it.

Effects can often be achieved for an occasion or a photograph that wouldn't be possible on a daily basis, e.g., hair that's too short to 'go up' can be coaxed over padding or have a piece added, but it is costly, as it takes time and expertise. Equally, long hair can be made to look short; this is easier as it can be wrapped, plaited, twisted or folded away, giving the effect of a tiny head. And, the back is all-important.

Many styles totally unsuited to modern daily life still look wonderful with a wedding or ball dress, but only on those occasions; for that, a good hairdresser will want to know what kind of head-dress, hat or veil is going to be worn, they will also want to know what jewellery, if any, is going to be worn and the design of the dress before suggesting a hair style.

Particularly for weddings, it is a good idea to have a complete dress rehearsal, if possible, as no one wants to be worried that their hair will fall down under the weight of an antique lace veil, or that the head-dress or decoration will not be secured firmly enough if there is a sudden gust of wind.

Uli Rose

Special Occasions: Style and Decoration

John Swannell

Wigs and Hairpieces

Wigs have been in existence for centuries – the ancient Egyptians, Greeks and Romans wore them, Elizabeth I had over eighty and throughout history they have played an important part in fashion.

Today, they are much in demand as a holiday accessory – to cover hair if it doesn't look too good after a day in the sun or in water; as an amusing part of the fashion scene, in brilliant colours far removed from natural hair; and as a cover-up for people with hair problems, from limp, oily, fine hair to complete baldness. Provided that they fit properly and are well styled, they are lightweight, easy to wear and less and less obviously wigs. They have another use too – they are an excellent way to try out a new hair style. Before cutting off all your hair or spending months growing it, try on a wig and see if the style really suits you.

There are two ways to buy a wig now – they can still be ordered, made-to-measure and probably of real hair, from your hairdresser. These are hand-made and obviously fit better and are therefore the most satisfactory, but they are also expensive and need professional cleaning and setting by a hairdresser. The alternative is to choose from the vast selection of ready-made wigs available at hairdressers and most department stores. Most of these are made from synthetic fibres, which have the advantage of being able to withstand rain, sleet, snow and humidity (one of the arch-enemies of hair). And when you wash them there's no need to worry about setting as they will revert to their original shape as they dry. They need minimal care, but between washes and when they're not being worn, they can be hung on a doorknob, turned inside out for airing, or stored in a box wrapped in tissue paper. They shouldn't be squashed or near too much heat. Give the wig a good brush or comb through every two or three days and shampoo regularly. Swish through in cool suds, rinse in cold water and drip-dry on a wig block if possible.

When you try on a wig you must take time to get it on properly. Ideally your own hair should be pinned in flat curls so that there is nothing to interfere with the shape of the wig and so you don't upset the angle by tucking in loose strands of your own hair. Put a wig on from the front, holding it firm on the forehead (it's easier if you get a friend to help the first time) while you ease it down on both sides and at the back. Then adjust it to fit securely – it should be firm but not tight, and you can always secure it on the crown with hairpins if necessary. Unless the style has a fringe, it is a good idea to fit the wig half an inch or so back from your face, then blend in your own hair over the edge of the wig. When you wear a wig it's rather like a close-fitting hat – the scalp heat is enclosed, the glands start producing more oil and the pores sweat. Therefore, if you suffer from any scalp disorder such as dandruff, it will become worse; also, your hair will quickly become lank, even if it was clean when you put the wig on. Because of this build-up of heat, it is vital to keep your hair and scalp clean – wash it daily if you are wearing a wig every day – and to wash or clean the wig regularly too. A dirty wig will spread infection very quickly. However often you wear a wig, you must give your scalp time to breathe. Prolonged covering by a wig can cause hair loss and scalp disorders.

Extra pieces or falls of hair are marvellous for occasional use, to increase the volume of the hair or add to a chignon, for instance. But because they have to be pinned very tightly to the real hair, they are potentially more damaging than wigs and should be used as rarely as possible. Hairpieces made of synthetic fibre are as satisfactory as real hair and can be cared for at home in the same way as wigs; those made by hand out of real hair need professional cleaning and styling by a hairdresser.

You and Your Hairdresser

The key to being happy with the way your hair looks is a good relationship with your hairdresser. However brilliant a hairdresser is – or you think he or she must be from seeing pictures of their work in newspapers and magazines – it is rare that you will obtain the perfect style the first time you visit the salon, although they will surely do their very best to make a new client happy and give the best possible cut.

Very often it is only after they have done your hair for several weeks, re-cut it, styled it for everyday and special occasions, seen (and heard from you) how it behaves away from their care, that you and they will begin to understand what is best for you and your hair. You must build up an atmosphere of mutual trust – you can expect thorough shampooing, advice on conditioning, colouring, permanent waving, straightening and all aspects of hair style and care. In return they need to learn how much time you devote to looking after your hair, how good you are at doing it yourself, what kind of life you lead, whether you eat and drink sensibly, sleep enough, exercise enough – in fact how much you really care about your looks generally. In time, you will learn to live with the hair you have and your hairdresser will teach you not to force your hair into shapes it cannot hold but to be happy if it's in the best possible condition and behaving as well as it possibly can. These days few women go daily to a hairdresser for a 'comb-out' or even regularly for a shampoo and set; the modern approach is to go once every four or five weeks for a cut, regularly for a conditioning treatment, whenever it is necessary to adjust or change the colour – and occasionally for a special event. A regular cut is one of the best beauty investments you can make – it keeps hair in shape, ensures that the ends don't dry out and split and makes it as easy as possible to look after at home. A professional conditioning treatment is also worthwhile – even women who have cared for their hair properly all their lives find that the condition sometimes deteriorates as a result of sickness (and intake of drugs), the stress of long-distance travel, climatic variations and over-exposure to the elements, or over-use of electrical aids like hair-driers and heated rollers; for them, a deep conditioning treatment at a salon can be of enormous benefit.

Clients should listen carefully to their hairdressers' advice before rushing headlong into a new cut, perm or drastic change of colour – the chances are that what they've got in mind has nothing to do with what would be successful with their type of hair or what would suit them; a good hairdresser will be able to suggest changes that *are* possible, and *will* suit them, and will therefore give them the new look and change they crave.

An expert hairdresser never stops learning from his clients – using their experiences to help others with similar situations or problems. A jet-setter, for instance, whom he sees regularly, although perhaps only every six months, is usually full of tips and tales on how to cope with hair in whatever climate and place she's just visited – and whether local hairdressers are good, bad or indifferent, whether she wished her hair had been a different length or whether it was just right for once: information invaluable to the next client, who is just off to that part of the world. A mother (who is a long-standing client) may bring in a teenage daughter who needs persuading that she'll regret a hard, geometric cut with her pretty, soft features – and a clever hairdresser who has known her, or about her, will succeed in giving her a cut to make everyone happy.

Permanent Waving and Straightening

Perming and straightening, even more than colouring, are potentially dangerous to the hair's health, because they alter the basic, natural structure of the hair shaft. It is absolutely vital that the processes are done with immense care and great expertise. When hair is wet it is in a relaxed, pliable state and can sometimes be stretched to as much as one third more than its original length before breaking – but it shrinks as it dries and will have returned to normal length by the time it is completely dry.

If you want to curl it temporarily, it is necessary to wet or dampen it and wind it round rollers or pipe-cleaners, tie it in rags or secure it in flat pin curls. When it has dried, the hair will be curly and remain so until wetted again – either intentionally or in a rainstorm, a humid climate or a steamy bathroom. Wet hair is obviously very vulnerable to breakage – which is why it should never be brushed – and should be treated with the greatest care and just coaxed into shape. The alternative to this method is to use heated rollers, which force the hair to accept a new direction, but the curl will still fall out when it becomes wet or damp. The disadvantage of this method is that it dries out the ends of the hair shaft, but it is very convenient. Permanent waving takes the temporary curling process a huge step further by *sealing* the shaft's new direction with the aid of chemicals, so that it doesn't disappear the next time the hair is soaked. These chemicals penetrate the cuticle of the hair shaft, enter the cortex and alter the natural line of the hair to a soft wave or tight curl, depending on the size of the roller the hair is wrapped around when the perm solution is applied. A soft, wavy result is often called a body wave, medium curls a straightforward perm and the frizzy variety an 'Afro', but they are all achieved by the process of permanent waving and will grow out as the hair grows from the roots and the ends are cut off. The danger of permanent waving lies in timing. Whether the perm is done at home or in a salon, precise timing is essential if the hair is not to be damaged by over-processing. This means that it can be literally dissolved by leaving the perm solution on too long, break off at the roots or become over-dry, not only at the ends but right down the hair shaft. Total concentration is required from the person doing the perm – kitchen timers are very useful to make sure the process is stopped at the appropriate moment. If perming at home is chosen, read every word of the manufacturers' instructions and follow them in every detail. No hair should be permed more often than every three or four months; if tinted, it should not be permed within two weeks either way of the colouring process; and hair that is in any way damaged already should not be permed at all.

Straightening is probably the most drastic thing that can be done to hair – it employs the perming process in reverse, i.e., instead of allowing the hair to shrink into a sealed wave, it stretches the hair straight and seals that straightness.

Because hair breaks even more easily when wet and stretched, straightening must only be done by an expert and only on hair that is strong enough in both texture and condition to take the strong chemicals employed. Instead of winding the hair round rollers when the perm solution is applied, the hair is gently combed straight from as close to the roots as possible, relaxing it and easing it into straightness. This combing must continue until the desired shape is achieved and the solution rinsed off.

The result will last until the hair is cut, but the straight effect will be reduced as the new hair shafts grow naturally curly from the root. Straightening is therefore not so successful as perming from a long-term point of view.

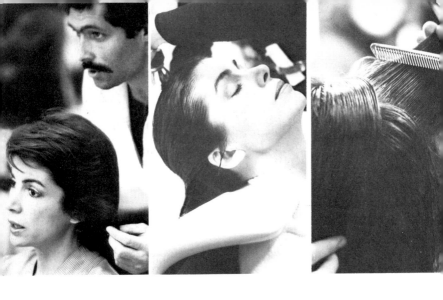

Straight to Curly: Perming your Hair

1. The author discusses her cut and shape with her hairdresser. **2.** Pre-perm shampoo and conditioning. **3.** Hair cut: volume removed with reverse layering technique – starting at the front with straight fringe to get the right length, and not have it fall too heavily or square on top – and moving straight to the back, leaving the longest hair behind the ears and at the nape. **4.** Hair examined for texture, correct perming lotion chosen. **5.** Hair curled section by section, using the normal method with curling rods and papers. **6.** Hair curled from the front backwards, as

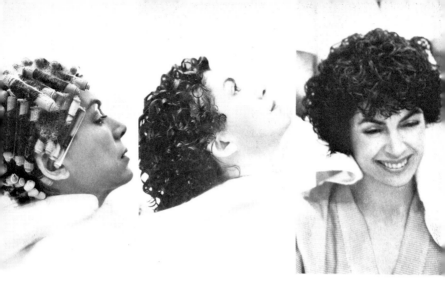

hair is to move back off the face. **7.** *Forty minutes later, over to the backwash for ten minutes of neutralizing with the curlers in.* **8.** *Five minutes more with curlers removed and hair loose.* **9.** *After thorough rinse and condition, hair rough-dried with towel.* **10.** *Dried with Air-Stop attachment on a hand drier to avoid static electricity, and give maximum body.* **11.** *While being dried, hair is shaped with fingers.* **12.** *A completely new look, as hair is lifted away from the face, the perm giving it body and movement.*

Sandra Lousada

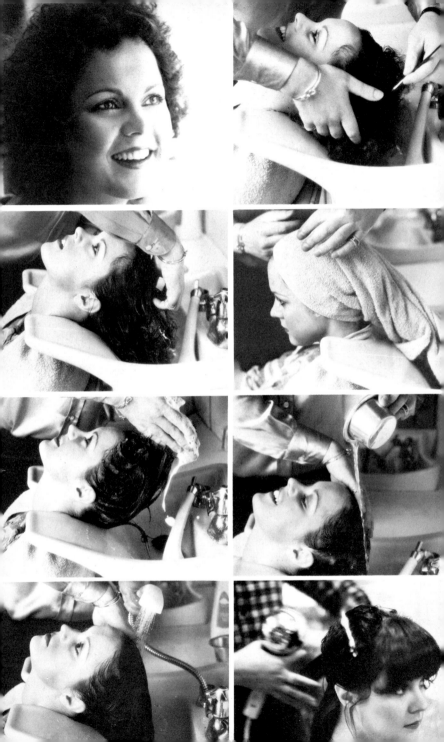

Curly to Straight

1. OPPOSITE, TOP LEFT *Model's hair in its natural state, curling tightly back from the face.* **2.** OPPOSITE, TOP RIGHT *The hair is to be straightened: first a 'relaxer' cream is painted onto the hair, with a brush.* **3.** *The cream is combed carefully through, and the hair is wrapped in a towel to warm the relaxing process.* **4.** *The hair is thoroughly shampooed.* **5.** *Then neutralised for ten minutes.* **6 and 7.** *Finally it is thoroughly conditioned and rinsed.* **8.** *Hair is blow dried.* **9.** ABOVE *The new straightened hair looks thicker and a richer brown, because the light was not getting through the curls. It also lengthened out to a head of hair to the shoulders with a full fringe.*

An A–Z of Hair Health

Allergies

Allergies resulting in a rash on the skin can appear on the scalp as easily as anywhere else on the body. Identifying the cause is often difficult, as there are hundreds of known, and many unknown, allergens. Use a mild shampoo as often as necessary and try not to aggravate the condition by scratching.

Alopecia

Alopecia areata, Alopecia totalis, traction Alopecia and banded Alopecia are various kinds of hair loss. *Alopecia areata* is loss of hair in patches and can develop into *Alopecia totalis*, or complete baldness. *Traction* and *banded Alopecia* result from an intolerable strain being put on the hair – from being pulled back into a tight ponytail or being pulled as it is straightened – and usually occur around the hairline. If this pressure is removed there is every chance the hair will regrow, but if the abuse continues the hair loss may be permanent.

Anaemia

Of the various varieties of anaemia, those caused by poor diet, lack of iron or vitamin deficiency (particularly vitamin B) will most affect the hair. Once the condition is halted, treated, and the diet improved, hair too will gradually return to health.

Bad Hair Odour

This usually occurs in conjuction with excessively oily hair conditions. It is the result of sweat- and oil-glands overproducing, often because of stress, exhaustion and a diet too rich in oily and fried foods. Once the diet is corrected, the oily hair condition treated and the stress alleviated, the odour will disappear.

Baldness

Baldness, or Alopecia totalis, occurs when the hair follicles atrophy and cease to produce new hair. It usually begins with a thinning of the hair at the temples and crown, becoming more severe until only the sides and back of the head have any hair at all – and sometimes not even these areas are covered. Baldness is often hereditary; it used to be thought peculiar to men, but nowadays many women suffer from it – reinforcing the theory that frequently it is caused by stress and strain and is also sometimes the result of illness or drugs.

Cortisone

This very powerful drug has many side effects; among them are distressing hair loss on the head and the reverse: growth of facial hair. The best answer for the former is a wig – there are such good ones available now in so many colours and styles that they can do wonders for the morale. As for the latter, if the facial hair isn't too coarse or dark, try a facial hair bleach or a depilatory cream especially formulated for facial hair.

Dandruff

This term is used widely to describe any scaly condition of the scalp. It is often thought to be the result of a dry scalp, and this can be so, but more often it goes hand in hand with oily hair when the sebaceous glands are over-producing and the follicles get blocked. Causes include lack of fresh air or air circulation, i.e., if wigs are worn constantly or the head is often wrapped in scarves or covered with a hat; stress and emotional strain; and sudden changes in climate or diet. The scalp should be kept immaculately clean by frequent washing. Many anti-dandruff shampoos contain harsh

73

ingredients, so it is sometimes suggested that a mild shampoo should be used alternately every other day with an anti-dandruff treatment. In other words, treat the condition with great gentleness: don't rub too hard or use anything too strong; wash frequently and rinse very thoroughly.

Dermatitis
This inflammation of the skin or scalp is also known as eczema.

Discoid Lupus Erythematosis
Related to dandruff, this condition appears as reddish-brown scaly patches with thinning hair in the centre and needs help from a doctor or dermatologist.

Drugs
Many medicines, even mild ones if taken over a long period of time, but particularly powerful modern drugs, cause the hair condition to change, the scalp to develop problems, or hair loss. If it is not possible to stop the medication, extra care must be taken over what food is eaten; shampoo and condition to keep the hair as healthy as possible; often vitamin supplements such as Brewers' Yeast tablets will help.

Dry Hair
Dry hair appears dull and brittle and is often caused by over-bleaching, perming or over-exposure to sun, wind, salt or chlorine-filled water. See also pages 17ff.

Eczema
This is a scalp disorder, also known as dermatitis, which is usually a reddish inflammation with damp, sometimes oozing, scales and which requires urgent attention from a doctor, dermatologist or trichologist.

Favus
This is a deep-rooted fungal infection, sometimes the result of ringworm left untreated for too long, affecting the scalp and sometimes the nails. It appears as yellow cup-like crusts, which stick together, then drop off, leaving the scalp hairless and scarred. Immediate attention from a doctor is essential.

Grey Hair
Grey hair, correctly defined, is hair where white hairs are mixed with the natural colour, giving a grey effect. If hair strands contain melanin (colour granules), they are 'coloured'; if they don't, they are 'white'. As the body ages, the hair bulbs fail to produce melanin in the hair shaft and white hair results. See also page 25ff.

Hair Breakage
Hair usually breaks only when it is dry and brittle and this comes from abuse: over-processing by means of bleach, colour or permanent waves or over-exposure to the elements. Hair that is breaking is very fragile and needs the gentlest treatment to restore it to health; it should be combed gently with a wide-toothed comb, shampooed with a richer formula than usual and conditioned every time it is washed. Don't blow-dry or use heated rollers or other electric aids until it has returned to health – and only with the greatest caution even then.

Hair Fall
A hair that has fallen has a tiny white bulb at one end. Fifty to a hundred hairs falling out daily is normal – hair loss over and above that needs treatment. The causes are not all known but include contraceptive pills, chemotherapy, drugs like cortisone, anything that interferes with hormones, and emotional disorders such as anxiety, lack of sleep or tension. Finding the cause will determine how permanent the loss will be – often the excessive fall can be halted and the hair will regrow in time.

Hormones
Hormones affect the hair – a proper balance must be maintained or problems may arise. Hormones are used to treat baldness in men, but the side effects may be unattractive and the results uncertain.

Ichthyosis
This is a hereditary condition where the skin is abnormally dry and scaly – hence its other name, Fish Skin. If it appears on the scalp, it will mean the hair becomes so dry and fragile it cannot grow to any length and will break off in clumps. It needs medical attention and frequent washing with a mild shampoo to keep the scalp clean.

Lice
Lice, even today, are quite common, usually among schoolchildren. A child with lice in the hair will probably complain of an itching scalp and scratch it excessively. Examine the scalp under a good light, paying particular attention to the hairline; if moving lice or eggs are visible, immediate medical attention is required. A doctor will prescribe an anti-louse shampoo, which should be applied by an adult who will see it is used correctly.

Menopause
At this stage in women's lives, when menstruation ceases, the hormone balance is changing and can cause hair loss and neurodermatitis, a patchy form of dandruff.

Menstruation
The menstrual cycle affects the sebaceous glands and the amount of oil they produce; consequently, many women find their hair oilier at the beginning and end of their period.

Mixed Condition Hair
Mixed condition hair appears as an oily scalp and dry hair. See also pages 18f.

Neurodermatitis
This is usually a clearly defined patch of really heavy dandruff-like scales at the nape of the neck, and is very itchy. The scalp next to it is quite often clean and healthy, but the patch needs urgent treatment. This condition is most prevalent among older women, often appearing during the menopause and after.

Oily Hair
Oily hair becomes lank and greasy even a few hours after shampooing; it is caused by over-productive sebaceous glands and can also produce bad hair odour. See also pages 16f.

The Pill
As with any other medicine that affects the hormones, contraceptive pills can be the cause of hair problems: a woman may experience excessive hair loss either while she is on the pill or when she comes off it. The pill can also cause a dry scalp and excessively oily hair.

Pityriasis
This is a loose term used for a bran-like or scaly appearance of the skin. *Pityriasis steatoides* and *pityriasis capitis* are alternative names for common dandruff. *Pityriasis amientacea* is a more virulent form of dandruff, which gathers along the hair shaft as well as over the scalp. Pityriasis should not be left untreated as hair loss will quickly follow.

Pregnancy and After-effects
Most pregnant women find their hair is healthier, shinier and more abundant during this time of increased oestrogen production; usually problems like oily hair are lessened or disappear. But from three to six months after the birth of the child the mother frequently suffers from hair loss. This hair loss is quite normal and the hair should soon recover; if the loss persists a trichologist should be consulted.

Psoriasis

This is a skin condition that manifests itself in red patches covered in silvery scales, which can also appear on the scalp. It doesn't itch but treatment so far is fairly unsuccessful – a shampoo containing tar may help.

Ringworm

This is a fungal infection of the skin; the scalp variety is known as *tinea capitis* and begins as a small papule, spreading concentrically and leaving scaly bald patches. It may have a pink centre. The sufferer should be immediately taken to a doctor, who will prescribe an antibiotic which will cure the ringworm.

Split Ends

Split ends are the result of hair abuse. Too much colouring, bleaching, perming or exposure to sun, wind and water produces damaged hair. Once hair has become split nothing can be done and the ends must be cut off and extra care taken with conditioning to restore health.

Thyroid Imbalance

Like hormonal, nutritional or any other glandular imbalance, this can cause hair loss, sudden dryness or lank hair.

Transplants

Hair transplants expertly done by cosmetic surgeons can be very successful; the technique is well-proven.

Trichotillomania

This is the name for the mania for pulling out one's hair – usually found in adolescent girls and menopausal women. See also page 23f.

Unwanted Hair

Hair grows on most parts of the body – more profusely on some people than others – and causes distress if it is very dark or thick on the face, arms, legs or around the pubic area. Isolated hairs can be pulled out with tweezers. A medium growth on legs, arms or face (particularly around the upper lip) can be bleached, which will make it less obvious, or waxed away. Waxing is also the most satisfactory way of achieving a clean bikini-line. Legs and under-arms can be shaved. The only permanent way of removing superfluous hair is by electrolysis, which is time-consuming, must be done by an expert and can be enormously expensive.

Zinc

Zinc Pyrithione is an ingredient in many effective anti-dandruff shampoos.

Ways to Colour Your Hair

The natural colour of your hair is determined by the melanin in the hair shaft. Melanin is the name for the pigment granules in the shaft – there is sometimes a small amount present in the medulla (the innermost of the three layers that compose a strand of hair), but most is in the cortex or middle layer. The darker your hair, the darker the melanin. Your natural hair colour is decided in the womb, but much can be done to improve or alter it if you wish. If you don't like your natural colour, you can change it. You can have any colour you want, but to change the colour for good means tampering with the structure of the hair shaft, which is potentially dangerous if it is not done with infinite care. Modern techniques have made it easier, but it is still essential to have some basic understanding of the process. The outer layer of the hair shaft, or cuticle, is made of fine overlapping cells, which must be lifted in order to get colour to penetrate and reach the cortex, where the pigment granules can be altered. The only way to do this is to use a permanent form of colouring called a dye or tint. There are other, less drastic, levels of colouring, which are satisfactory and great fun, particularly for the young, who like to change their looks as often as their moods.

Colouring processes fall into three main groups: temporary, semi-permanent and permanent.

Temporary Colour
Temporary colour or water rinsing is the mildest process. The colour will only cling to the outer layer (the cuticle), contains no bleaching agent or penetrating ingredient to alter the natural

Colouring your Hair

1. ABOVE LEFT *The model's hair was a pretty blond but out of condition from the sun and years of colouring and bleaching.* **2.** ABOVE RIGHT *The hair must be coloured red to replace artificial pigment. This allows the hair to absorb the new colour. Without it the new brown would rinse away at the first wash.* **3.** *First the highlights are brushed with red pigment: they are most in need as they have been the most bleached. This is left on for thirty minutes.* **4.** *Pigment is combed through the hair.*

Sandra Lousada

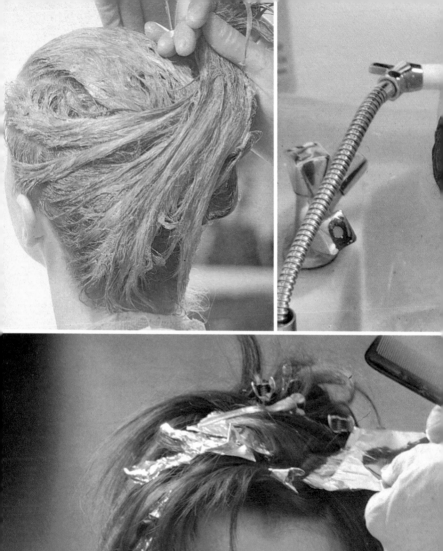

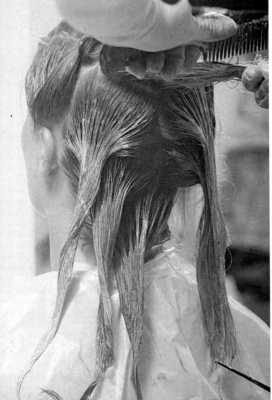

5. TOP LEFT *Colour is massaged through hair to make sure of a natural blending.*
6. TOP RIGHT *The hair is rinsed and dried.*
7. *The hair is lightened by delicately streaking with a combination of four different blonds for a natural, subtle effect. A section of the hair is taken up, and several strands are lifted from it which are then brushed with colour, wrapped in foil and left until the colour takes hold. The result is a head strewn with fine blond lights.*
8. *Conditioner is applied every time the hair is rinsed.*

Sandra Lousada

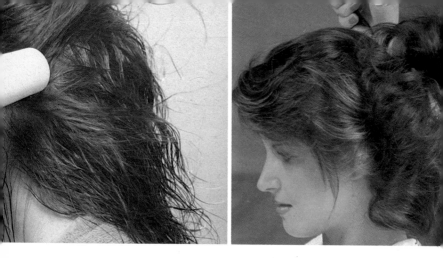

9. ABOVE LEFT *The hair is rinsed and dried for the last time.* **10.** ABOVE RIGHT *Then it is brushed into a soft knot.* **11.** BELOW *The hair is transformed by the careful treatment it has received. It has regained its glow of health.*

colour underneath and will disappear during the next shampoo. A colour rinse will only change the tone of the hair – shading it up or down – not the actual colour. Colour rinses are useful for improving tinted hair between applications, if the hair has faded in the sun or become brassy from bleaching – but should not be used too often for this purpose, as the coating on the cuticle may have a dulling effect over the tint. They are excellent for cleaning and brightening the tone of grey or white hair but will do nothing to cover it up.

Temporary colours are usually applied after shampooing and normally need no skin-patch test, as they are hypo-allergenic. They are simple to apply at home, but read the instructions carefully.

Semi-Permanent Colour

Semi-permanent colourants provide a medium amount of colour intensity but contain no bleaching agent so cannot alter the basic colour. They *do* contain a penetrating agent, so the depth of colour within the limits of the natural range can be altered. This depth will gradually fade away in four to six weeks, a little intensity being lost every time the hair is shampooed, until it returns to its original shade. Thus, they can enrich mouse-brown, polish a dull blond, enhance the red tones in brown hair, reduce or reveal the copper tone in red hair.

Semi-permanent colourants are useful for disguising the first grey hairs, but the effect will be more like highlighting, as there is only a certain amount of coverage; once the grey hairs become the majority, a permanent tint is the only way to cover them satisfactorily. Like temporary rinses, they usually have a built-in conditioner and are therefore useful in revitalizing dull hair – giving it added colour and lustre.

Semi-permanent colour is fairly easy to apply at home, but it is necessary to carry out a skin-patch test twenty-four hours beforehand and to follow the instructions exactly.

Permanent Colour

All permanent colourants have a toxic base and it is therefore essential to carry out a skin-patch test twenty-four hours in advance, whether you are planning to do the tint at home or to have it done by a professional colourist. It is also a good idea to do a 'strand test' at the same time. A hairdresser will normally do a skin-patch test behind your ear, but if you are colouring your hair at home, the inside of the elbow is easier to reach and observe. A small amount of tint should be mixed and applied to the skin – about a square inch is enough – and left for twenty-four hours, making sure it isn't rubbed or washed off. If there is any reaction at all, don't use the product. The strand test is done like this: cut off 30–40 strands of hair from different parts of the head, close to the scalp; using the remainder of the product used for the patch test, follow the instructions to the letter. Then study the results in strong daylight. Remember that everyone's hair colour is different, so the result is unlikely to be identical with that on the packet. What happens to those few test strands will happen to your entire head, so be sure you are happy with the colour before going ahead.

Permanent colourants – or dyes or tints, which are all more or less the same – contain both penetrating and bleaching agents (to reach through the cuticle and alter the pigment granules in the cortex) and, of course, the colour the hair is going to become (called an oxidation dye), which is mixed with the bleach. The bleach strips the granules of colour and makes the cortex porous and ready to absorb the dye and produce the change of colour. It is possible to achieve good results with permanent tints for home use, providing the colour is not to be changed too much, but, for really satisfactory effects and dramatic switches of colour, permanent tints are best applied in a salon, where the colourist can mix individual shades and time the process exactly according to the hair's texture. Fine hair absorbs colour more readily, coarse hair resists it. The only way colouring can go wrong is if it is wrongly applied. If this happens, not only will the colour be a surprise, but the hair can be badly damaged. Therefore, it is vital that permanent hair colour, whether applied at home or in a salon, is used correctly. If you are thinking of a radical alteration in your hair colour – changing from brunette or blond to red, for instance – it is a good idea to try on some wigs of the colour you have in mind. This will give you a chance to see if it really suits you and to discuss it with the colourist who is going to apply the tint. He or she will be trained in colour blending as well as application and give expert advice on the suitability of the colour you have chosen.

Bleaching on its own decolourizes the hair and gives an old-fashioned solid-white blond effect. It is much prettier on a whole head when used with several shades of tint for a more natural multi-toned effect. Bleaching is a vital part of the permanent tinting process, as it is necessary to remove the existing natural colour before imposing a new one. Done correctly, it will cause no damage to the hair, but over-bleaching makes the hair excessively dry, brittle and prone to breakage and split ends.

Streaking, highlighting and *tipping* all use a bleaching process.

Streaking involves narrow ribbons of light colour usually applied round the face, following the movement of the hair or the line of the cut. The bleach is painted on in lines down the full length of the hair, left until the desired shade is obtained, then rinsed thoroughly and either combined with a toning rinse or shampooed with the rest of the hair and conditioned.

Highlighting, sometimes called *frosting*, usually involves drawing small sections of hair through holes in a plastic cap, applying the bleach to these strands and wrapping them in tinfoil. (It can also be done without the plastic cap, just using tinfoil.) The advantage of this method is that the bleach is kept at different distances from the scalp and roots of the hair, so that as the hair grows out it blends in with the natural hair and doesn't leave an ugly regrowth line. When the desired colour is reached, the tinfoil and/or cap are removed, the bleach rinsed off and the whole head either toned with a semi-permanent toner, or shampooed and conditioned.

Tipping, sometimes called *feathering*, means that the bleach is just applied to the ends. Again the plastic cap with holes may be used, although on short hair the bleach is often painted on. This is most effective if two or three shades are chosen.

It is difficult to do any of these lightening effects successfully at home as they rely on the precise application of the bleach – faultless timing and shading-in with the rest of the hair – which is best left in the hands of the expert colourist. But with the help of a friend you may achieve a satisfactory result.

Hair should not be permanently waved for at least two weeks before or after tinting.

Natural Vegetable Dyes

Natural vegetable dyes are non-toxic and do not interfere with the structure of the hair. They cling to the cuticle or outer layer and do not penetrate the cortex or middle layer. They leave the hair shining and full of body. It usually takes several applications to achieve a colour that would be reached in one salon visit and one application of modern tint.

Henna has been used as a hair colourant for centuries and has recently become enormously popular with the revival of interest in herbal medicine, natural cosmetics and general health-consciousness. Henna dye is made from the *Lawsonia alba* plant which grows all along the North African coast and into the Middle East, from Morocco to Iran. The Moroccan henna is the lightest in colour and conditioning value, the Iranian the richest, being deeper red and full of conditioning properties and therefore the most sought after. The leaves of the plant are dried, then crushed into a powder, which is mixed with water. (Some colourists like to use black coffee or other naturally coloured liquids, and add lemon juice or vinegar to the paste.)

Henna reacts differently not only on different coloured hair, but also on the same hair under different conditions. Therefore, it is essential to make a strand test before commencing the application.

Try experimenting. It is possible to henna your hair red, rich brown with shades of red highlights or deep chestnut. The best results are obtained with hair that is naturally brunette or black, and the new colour will last several months.

For the best results go to a professional colourist, who will know what results are likely to be achieved with your hair colour as well as the source of the henna and how much orange-red pigment it contains. If you want to just brighten and condition your hair at home, try one of the temporary shampoos, which will add gloss and highlights and give you some idea of whether you want a stronger, more permanent change. As natural henna is non-toxic, it is not necessary to do a skin-patch test first and it is very useful for people with sensitive skins. Henna should never be used on hair that has been chemically tinted – it is even more difficult to control the resulting tone of the colour – and is not very satisfactory as a covering for grey hair, as it is likely to turn orange. Compound hennas are available, but these contain metallic substances and should be used according to the instructions – they should not be treated as natural vegetable dyes or be expected to work in the same way.

Camomile, when infused, has a lightening effect on hair and is most successful on blond or naturally fair hair. Depending on the strength of the infusion and the number of times it is applied, it will produce a colour from pale to bright yellow.

Marigold applied as an infusion will impart soft reddish-yellow tones to highly bleached or white hair.

Saffron – the root, not the powder used in cooking – can give a bright yellow tint to fair or blond hair but needs many applications. The dye is made by boiling the root for at least half an hour.

Sage should be infused like camomile and will dull grey hair, producing a brown tone. Mix it with strong tea for a darker colour.

Walnut will also give a brown tone to grey hair. The colourant is obtained by boiling walnuts for several hours and using the result-ing liquid as a rinse, which can be stored and used when needed.

Hair and Diet

Whatever your age, if you want healthy hair, you must eat properly. Diet is the most effective way to control hair health – the good things are the natural foods, fresh fruit and vegetables, proteins, lots of water, plus extra vitamin B in the form of Brewers' Yeast tablets. The bad things are too many dairy products, animal fat, sugar, salt and spices – spices create no problem in a hot climate but in cooler places can be the cause of scalp problems.

It's up to parents to make sure that babies and children are well-nourished, but after that it's up to you – and it's not just your hair that benefits; your whole body will function better and you will feel that much fitter and more energetic. This kind of diet has nothing to do with slimming – it's a balanced way of eating for a lifetime; following it, your weight should remain stable and your hair healthy.

Work out your eating plan on a daily basis, using the following as a guide line. GOOD for you are:

Protein: lean meat for vitamin E, and liver (once a week) for vitamin B; fish for iron and vitamin A; eggs (but one a day is enough) for vitamin B and vitamin D, which is also found in liver and tuna fish.
Fresh vegetables: particularly green ones like spinach and broccoli for vitamin C; carrots for vitamin A. (Make it a rule to cook vegetables lightly to keep all the goodness intact.)
Salad: all the greens and raw vegetables such as lettuce, tomatoes and endive for vitamin A; watercress, mustard, spinach and

cauliflower for vitamin K; celery, radishes, carrots and avocados for iron. (You can make a delicious meal from a bowl of salad – add a few nuts for vitamin E and currants for more iron.)

Fresh fruit: lots of it and whatever is in season.

Roughage: wholewheat cereal, or bran or wholemeal bread (use polyunsaturated margarine rather than butter) for vitamin B; brown rice for vitamins E and B; baked potatoes for vitamin C inside and iron in the skin.

Liquid: lots of water, at least six glasses a day.

Sweetening: honey when possible.

AVOID, or cut out if you can, the following:

Milk and milk products like ice-cream, cream, sour cream, cheese.

Sugary items like cakes, biscuits, puddings, chocolates, sweets.

Salty items like potato crisps, pickles, sauces.

Over-processed foods like white bread, white sugar, white rice.

Fried foods (grilled, poached and baked are better).

Caffeine drinks (coffee, tea, colas).

Alcoholic drinks.

Cigarettes.

A nutritious, balanced diet should provide you with all the vitamins you need, but if you feel run-down, have been on antibiotics or for some reason your hair looks lack-lustre, take supplements of iron and vitamins B, C, K and E. Vitamins A and D should *not* be taken in supplementary pill form.

Recipes for Healthy Hair
Orange and Tomato Soup

2 lb (0.9 kg) ripe tomatoes
1 medium onion
1 medium carrot
1 bay leaf
8 peppercorns
1 small piece lemon rind
pinch salt
2 pints (1.1 ℓ) stock

$\frac{1}{2}$ oz (15 g) margarine
1 oz (30 g) plain flour
juice and rind of $\frac{1}{2}$ orange
1 small teaspoon sugar
1 carton natural unsweetened
   yogurt
fresh basil

Skin and remove pips from tomatoes. Place them with the peeled, sliced onion and carrot, bay leaf, peppercorns, lemon rind, salt and stock in a saucepan. Cover and bring to the boil, then simmer for half an hour. Put in the blender to liquidize, then return to the pan, adding margarine and flour; bring back to the boil and boil for 2–3 minutes (until thick), whisking continuously. Stir in grated orange rind, juice, sugar. Remove from heat and when cool stir in the yogurt. Garnish with chopped fresh basil. (Serves 6–8)

Tomato Jelly

2 tablespoons gelatine
1 pint (0.6 ℓ) tomato juice
2 lemons

$1\frac{1}{4}$ pints (0.7 ℓ) chicken stock
salt and pepper
Worcestershire sauce

Sprinkle gelatine on tomato juice in a heavy saucepan. Add grated rind of 1 lemon and the chicken stock. Bring slowly to the boil, stirring continuously; when boiling, lower the heat and cook for a further five minutes. Strain through a fine sieve and add pepper, salt, lemon juice and a dash of Worcestershire sauce. Put into a mould or individual cocotte dishes and set in refrigerator for 2–3 hours. Serve with chopped chives or a sauce of natural unsweetened yogurt seasoned with lemon juice, salt, pepper and cayenne. (Serves 6–8)

Cold Cucumber and Dill Soup
4 peeled cucumbers   2 pints (0.6 ℓ) chicken stock
2 tablespoons chopped fresh dill   large carton natural yogurt
salt and pepper

Make a purée of the cucumbers and pour into a large bowl. Add dill, salt, pepper and chicken stock. Stir well, then chill for several hours. Just before serving, add enough yogurt to get the desired consistency. Sprinkle a little extra dill on top. (Serves 6–8)

Crudités with Garlic Dip
Arrange a selection of fresh raw vegetables in a basket or bowl and place a small bowl of dip in the centre. A good mixture is cauliflower, fennel, radishes, carrots, celery and small tomatoes. For the dip, season a carton of natural unsweetened yogurt with salt and freshly ground black pepper and add a crushed clove of garlic.

Simple Starters
Serve ripe melons with a quarter of lemon instead of sugar.
Sprinkle avocado pears with salt and pepper and a squeeze of lemon juice.
Grill half a grapefruit with a tiny amount of thin honey.
Grate some carrots and dress them with orange juice, chopped mint, salt and pepper.

Green Bean and Prawn Salad
Combine cold cooked thin French beans with cold cooked artichoke hearts and place in a bowl. Surround with segments of fresh grapefruit and cover with prawns and a sprinkling of lumpfish roe. Season with salt, freshly ground black pepper and lemon juice. This makes an excellent lunch dish.

Risotto

12 oz (340 g) brown rice
1½ pints (0.9 ℓ) chicken stock
salt
5 oz (140 g) chopped onions
4 oz (115 g) margarine

4 oz (115 g) chopped tomatoes
4 oz (115 g) grated parmesan
   cheese
chopped fresh basil

Put rice in a pan with stock and a pinch of salt. Bring to the boil, cover tightly and simmer for 45 minutes. Meanwhile, cook the onion in the margarine until just turning brown and add the tomatoes just before combining with the cooked rice. Serve with grated cheese, a little chopped fresh basil, if it is in season, and a green salad. (Serves 6–8)

Grilled Chicken with Lemon
Rub a little oil over chicken pieces on both sides. Sprinkle with salt, pepper, rosemary and a good squeeze of lemon juice and grill well until cooked through, or bake slowly in the oven. Serve with small baked potatoes and lightly cooked courgettes.

Kedgeree

2–4 oz (55–115 g) margarine
16 oz (455 g) cooked flaked
   fish (one with a good
   flavour – salmon or smoked
   haddock, for instance)

4 cups cold boiled brown rice
salt and pepper
pinch of nutmeg
4 hard-boiled eggs
1 lemon

Melt the margarine and stir in the fish and rice. Season with salt, pepper and nutmeg and add chopped egg whites. Heat very gently until hot right through, then pile in a dish. Rub the egg yolks through a sieve and sprinkle over the top. Serve with lemon sections and a green salad. (Serves 6–8)

Baked Bananas
Peel and put in shallow oven-proof dish, pour over a little thin honey and lots of lemon juice and bake slowly.

Melon and Plum Salad

1 melon	10 oz (285 g) orange juice
1½ lb (0.7 kg) plums	2 oz (55 g) honey

Remove seeds from the melon, peel and cut the flesh into cubes. Wash, stone and cut the plums in segments. Mix the fruit and add the orange juice, in which the honey has been dissolved. Chill.

Baked Apples
Core the apples and put in a shallow oven-proof dish. Stuff the centres with honey, raisins, dates, cloves, cinnamon, marmalade. Sprinkle with a little brown sugar and add about a quarter of an inch of water. Bake in a moderate oven, basting occasionally, for about 45 minutes. Serve hot or cold.

Raspberry Ginger Cream

12 oz (340 g) fresh or frozen raspberries	ground ginger to taste
2 tablespoons thin honey	½ pint (0.3 ℓ) natural unsweetened yogurt

Thaw berries if frozen, drain thoroughly and separate. Mix honey, ginger and yogurt and fold in the raspberries gently. Chill for at least an hour. Before serving, stir again gently to blend in any juice.

Hair and Exercise A healthy body means healthy hair. Any routine of exercises will include some to rev up the circulation – this will benefit the hair most, bringing oxygen through the bloodstream to feed the hair follicles. Five or ten minutes a day will help, though a longer session is recommended. Exercises also relax the mind and body muscles and ease tension – all of which mean a general lessening of stress, one of hair's worst enemies.

Index